SRA Imagine It!

Lesson
Assessment
Book 1
Workbook

Level 1

SRAonline.com

 SRA

Send all inquiries to this address:
SRA/McGraw-Hill
4400 Easton Commons
Columbus, OH 43219-6188

ISBN: 978-0-07-613071-9
MHID: 0-07-613071-1

1 2 3 4 5 6 7 8 9   MAZ   13 12 11 10 09 08 07

The **McGraw·Hill** Companies

Table of Contents

Name _____ Date _____ Score _____

Sound Blending

1.

○   ○   ○

2.

○   ○   ○

3.

○   ○   ○

4.

      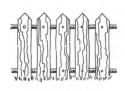

○   ○   ○

5.

○   ○   ○

Name _____ **Date** _____ **Score** _____

High-Frequency Words

1. san   can   cin
    ○   ○   ○

2. ov   un   on
    ○   ○   ○

3. am   aw   um
    ○   ○   ○

4. und   ard   and
    ○   ○   ○

5. thi   the   dhe
    ○   ○   ○

Name _____ **Date** _____ **Score** _____

Compare and Contrast

1.    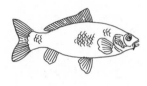   

                        ◯   ◯

2.       

                        ◯   ◯

3.       

                        ◯   ◯

4.       

                        ◯   ◯

5.       

                        ◯   ◯

Name _____ Date _____ Score _____

Word Boundaries

1. Hi, Tina.

     1   2   3

     ○   ○   ○

2. This is my mom.

     2   3   4

     ○   ○   ○

3. Mom, this is my friend.

     3   4   5

     ○   ○   ○

4. Her name is Tina.

     3   4   5

     ○   ○   ○

5. She is nice.

     2   3   4

     ○   ○   ○

Name _____ **Date** _____ **Score** _____

Dropping Final Sounds

1.

○   ○   ○

2.

○   ○   ○

3.

○   ○   ○

4.

      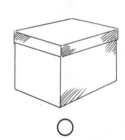

○   ○   ○

5.

○   ○   ○

Name _____ Date _____ Score _____

High-Frequency Words

1.   did   dod   pid
          ○   ○   ○

2.   ti   it   ut
          ○   ○   ○

3.   hud   hab   had
          ○   ○   ○

4.   hom   him   hin
          ○   ○   ○

5.   said   sied   sait
          ○   ○   ○

Name _____ **Date** _____ **Score** _____

Drawing Conclusions

1. swimming   hiking   skating

○   ○   ○

2. rainy   nice   snowy

○   ○   ○

3. dog   cat   horse

○   ○   ○

4. breakfast   lunch   dinner

○   ○   ○

5. ball   letter   pen

○   ○   ○

Name _____ **Date** _____ **Score** _____

Grammar, Usage, and Mechanics

1.   the   there   that

        ◯   ◯   ◯

2. The bird is flying.

        4   5   6

        ◯   ◯   ◯

3.   jump   red   truck

        ◯   ◯   ◯

4.   plane   fast   sit

        ◯   ◯   ◯

5.   hot   cat   know

        ◯   ◯   ◯

Name _____ Date _____ Score _____

Missing Sounds

1.   r   t   k
       ○   ○   ○

2.   n   t   m
       ○   ○   ○

3.   d   r   w
       ○   ○   ○

4.   l   s   n
       ○   ○   ○

5.   p   s   l
       ○   ○   ○

Name _____ **Date** _____ **Score** _____

High-Frequency Words

1.   haz   hos   has
       ○   ○   ○

2.   at   ot   ut
       ○   ○   ○

3.   un   in   ni
       ○   ○   ○

4.   there   thair   theer
       ○   ○   ○

5.   sey   sie   see
       ○   ○   ○

Name _____ Date _____ Score _____

Compare and Contrast

1.   ◯ 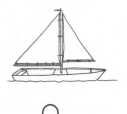 ◯

2.   ◯ ◯

3.   ◯  ◯

4.   ◯   ◯

5.  ◯ ◯

Name _____ Date _____ Score _____

Selection Vocabulary

1.

○   ○   ○

2.

○   ○   ○

3.

○   ○   ○

4.

○   ○   ○

5.

○   ○   ○

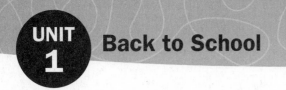

Name _____ **Date** _____ **Score** _____

Writing Assessment

Name _____ **Date** _____ **Score** _____

Syllables

1.   airplane   truck   wagon
          ○   ○   ○

2.   table   chair   desk
          ○   ○   ○

3.   friend   mom   sister
          ○   ○   ○

4.   balloon   animal   hurry
          ○   ○   ○

5.   happening   button   parade
          ○   ○   ○

Name _____ Date _____ Score _____

High-Frequency Words

1. san't   car't   can't
    ○   ○   ○

2. cill   call   koll
    ○   ○   ○

3. look   loke   loik
    ○   ○   ○

4. waz   was   wus
    ○   ○   ○

5. waht   whut   what
    ○   ○   ○

Name _____ Date _____ Score _____

Cause and Effect

1.　　rain　　　　　wind　　　　　flood
　　　○　　　　　　○　　　　　　○

2.　　feed　　　　　walk　　　　　puppy
　　　○　　　　　　○　　　　　　○

3.　　cut　　　　　step　　　　　bandage
　　　○　　　　　　○　　　　　　○

4.　　resting　　　winning　　　running
　　　○　　　　　　○　　　　　　○

5.　　showing　　　prize　　　　job
　　　○　　　　　　○　　　　　　○

Name _____ **Date** _____ **Score** _____

Print Recognition

1.   +   3   b
           ○   ○   ○

2.   c   M   7
           ○   ○   ○

3.   Jane   bend   grow
           ○   ○   ○

4.   v   6   k
           ○   ○   ○

5.   L   R   d
           ○   ○   ○

Name _____ **Date** _____ **Score** _____

Beginning Consonants

1.   g   b   j
   ○   ○   ○

2.   f   v   r
   ○   ○   ○

3.   z   p   s
   ○   ○   ○

4.   f   h   p
   ○   ○   ○

5.   n   k   g
   ○   ○   ○

Name _____ **Date** _____ **Score** _____

High-Frequency Words

1. bip   big   bij
    ○   ○   ○

2. got   gud   goc
    ○   ○   ○

3. tu   ti   to
    ○   ○   ○

4. ast   ask   ack
    ○   ○   ○

5. of   fo   uf
    ○   ○   ○

Name _____ **Date** _____ **Score** _____

Classify and Categorize

1.    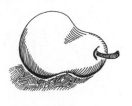   

    ○   ○   ○

2.    

    ○   ○   ○

3.    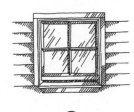   

    ○   ○   ○

4.       

    ○   ○   ○

5.       

    ○   ○   ○

Name _____ **Date** _____ **Score** _____

Grammar, Usage, and Mechanics

1.   dog   cats   bird
         ○   ○   ○

2.   at   tall   who
         ○   ○   ○

3.   cold   find   are
         ○   ○   ○

4.   boy's   shirt   blue
         ○   ○   ○

5.   Lucy   Lucys   Lucy's
         ○   ○   ○

Name _____ **Date** _____ **Score** _____

Ending Consonants

1.   x   k   t
      ○   ○   ○

2.   k   z   s
      ○   ○   ○

3.   b   g   d
      ○   ○   ○

4.   i   ck   p
      ○   ○   ○

5.   d   dge   b
      ○   ○   ○

Name _____ **Date** _____ **Score** _____

High-Frequency Words

1. dowr   doun   down
        ○   ○   ○

2. ef   if   af
        ○   ○   ○

3. its   ist   ids
        ○   ○   ○

4. rud   rev   red
        ○   ○   ○

5. hulp   help   helt
        ○   ○   ○

Name _____ **Date** _____ **Score** _____

Main Idea and Details

1.

○ ○ ○

2.

○ ○ ○

3.

○ ○ ○

4.

○ ○ ○

5.

○ ○ ○

Name _____ Date _____ Score _____

Selection Vocabulary

1.

○   ○   ○

2.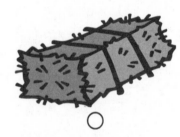

○   ○   ○

3.

○   ○   ○

4.

○   ○   ○

5.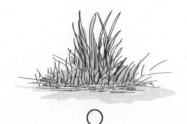

○   ○   ○

Name _____ Date _____ Score _____

Writing Assessment

Name _____ Date _____ Score _____

Phoneme Blending

1.

⚪ ⚪ ⚪

2.

⚪ ⚪ ⚪

3.

⚪ ⚪ ⚪

4.

⚪ ⚪ ⚪

5.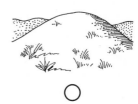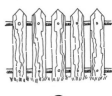

⚪ ⚪ ⚪

Name _____ Date _____ Score _____

High-Frequency Words

1. get   git   gat

○   ○   ○

2. dhat   that   thit

○   ○   ○

3. thiz   thos   this

○   ○   ○

4. for   fot   fer

○   ○   ○

5. owt   out   oud

○   ○   ○

Main Idea and Details

1.

○ ○ ○

2.

○ ○ ○

3.

○ ○ ○

4.

○ ○ ○

5.

○ ○ ○

Name _____ Date _____ Score _____

Punctuation and Type

1.   **.**   **?**   **!**
         ○   ○   ○

2.   **!**   **.**   **?**
         ○   ○   ○

3.   **?**   **!**   **.**
         ○   ○   ○

4.   **the**   are   *who*
         ○   ○   ○

5.   that   *will*   **must**
         ○   ○   ○

Name _____ Date _____ Score _____

Letters and Sounds

1.   thip   ship   slip
       ○   ○   ○

2.   bird   bord   bard
       ○   ○   ○

3.   bosh   bath   batch
       ○   ○   ○

4.   lamb   lamd   lamp
       ○   ○   ○

5.   star   stir   stur
       ○   ○   ○

Name _____ **Date** _____ **Score** _____

High-Frequency Words

1.   liddle   little   littel
     ○   ○   ○

2.   wint   wend   went
     ○   ○   ○

3.   will   wull   wiil
     ○   ○   ○

4.   whin   when   wenh
     ○   ○   ○

5.   girl   gril   gurl
     ○   ○   ○

Name _____ Date _____ Score _____

Making Inferences

1.
         ○   ○   ○

2.
         ○   ○   ○

3.
         ○   ○   ○

4.
         ○   ○   ○

5.
         ○   ○   ○

Name _____ **Date** _____ **Score** _____

Grammar, Usage, and Mechanics

1.   jump   will   throw
            ○   ○   ○

2.   th edog   thed og   the dog
            ○   ○   ○

3. the cat is black.   She is tall.   he can run.
            ○   ○   ○

4.   a cloud   the rainy day   It is sunny.
            ○   ○   ○

5.   in a room   We like to play. A bird can fly.
            ○   ○   ○

Name _____ **Date** _____ **Score** _____

Letters and Sounds

1. banth bangk bank
  ○ ○ ○

2. sinq sing sig
  ○ ○ ○

3. kwick quick qwuk
  ○ ○ ○

4. which wheck wuch
  ○ ○ ○

5. spart sporth sport
  ○ ○ ○

Name _____ **Date** _____ **Score** _____

High-Frequency Words

1.   an   ar   un
    ○   ○   ○

2.   shey   thay   they
    ○   ○   ○

3.   dut   but   lut
    ○   ○   ○

4.   do   du   de
    ○   ○   ○

5.   shi   che   she
    ○   ○   ○

Name _____ Date _____ Score _____

Cause and Effect

1.   riding   road   stone
      ○   ○   ○

2.   cat   bird   window
      ○   ○   ○

3.   sweating   riding   turning
      ○   ○   ○

4.   damp   hard   colors
      ○   ○   ○

5.   dry   rain   leaves
      ○   ○   ○

Name _____ Date _____ Score _____

Selection Vocabulary

1.

  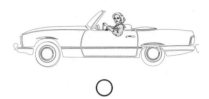

○　　　　　　　○　　　　　　　○

2.

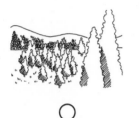  

○　　　　　　　○　　　　　　　○

3.

○　　　　　　　○　　　　　　　○

4.

○　　　　　　　○　　　　　　　○

5.

○　　　　　　　○　　　　　　　○

Name _____ **Date** _____ **Score** _____

Writing Assessment

_____

_____

_____

_____

_____

_____

_____

_____

_____

_____

_____

_____

_____

_____

_____

_____

Name _____ **Date** _____ **Score** _____

Letters and Sounds

1.	jam ○	yell ○	ran ○
2.	up ○	it ○	ape ○
3.	van ○	hat ○	fan ○
4.	dot ○	can ○	wet ○
5.	wish ○	fun ○	vent ○

Name _____ **Date** _____ **Score** _____

High-Frequency Words

1. aal all ull
○ ○ ○

2. wher wure were
○ ○ ○

3. with widt weth
○ ○ ○

4. yez yis yes
○ ○ ○

5. gump jump jumb
○ ○ ○

Name _____ **Date** _____ **Score** _____

Main Idea and Details

1. garage   ladder   bathroom
          ○   ○   ○

2. net   Nat   fish
          ○   ○   ○

3. coaches   teaches   writes
          ○   ○   ○

4. market   bookstore   home
          ○   ○   ○

5. toys   window   store
          ○   ○   ○

Name _____ **Date** _____ **Score** _____

Text and Illustration

1.

○   ○   ○

2.

○   ○   ○

3.

○   ○   ○

4.

○   ○   ○

5.

○   ○   ○

Name _____ **Date** _____ **Score** _____

Reviewing Short Vowels

1.   bat   shut   sit
         ○   ○   ○

2.   log   hit   mad
         ○   ○   ○

3.   van   win   mop
         ○   ○   ○

4.   top   wag   sun
         ○   ○   ○

5.   lap   met   wig
         ○   ○   ○

Name _____ Date _____ Score _____

High-Frequency Words

1.   ride   ribe   rede
         ○   ○   ○

2.   wulk   wolk   walk
         ○   ○   ○

3.   ve   we   wi
         ○   ○   ○

4.   well   wull   weel
         ○   ○   ○

5.   muke   mack   make
         ○   ○   ○

Name _____ Date _____ Score _____

Classify and Categorize

1. fox   seat   truck
    ○   ○   ○

2. sister   bunny   bicycle
    ○   ○   ○

3. foot   nose   shirt
    ○   ○   ○

4. happy   sunny   fast
    ○   ○   ○

5. rainy   silly   snowy
    ○   ○   ○

Name _____ Date _____ Score _____

Grammar, Usage, and Mechanics

1. on the floor   Where are you going?   This is my house.
        ○   ○   ○

2. Watch out!   What time is it?   I live on Walnut Street.
        ○   ○   ○

3. Bob is here.   What time is it?   We won the game!
        ○   ○   ○

4. Will we go today?   The test was long.   Stop writing now.
        ○   ○   ○

5. Come here, please.   Where is Mom?   Watch out!
        ○   ○   ○

Name _____ **Date** _____ **Score** _____

Letters and Sounds

1. plate   vine   stir

   ○   ○   ○

2. but   tide   shot

   ○   ○   ○

3. map   get   go

   ○   ○   ○

4. peg   use   pot

   ○   ○   ○

5. gave   game   giant

   ○   ○   ○

Name _____ **Date** _____ **Score** _____

High-Frequency Words

1.   over   uver   iver
           ○   ○   ○

2.   dhem   thim   them
           ○   ○   ○

3.   ufter   after   affer
           ○   ○   ○

4.   yue   yow   you
           ○   ○   ○

5.   like   likk   luke
           ○   ○   ○

Name _____ **Date** _____ **Score** _____

Reality and Fantasy

1.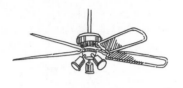
○ ○ ○

2.
○ ○ ○

3.
○ ○ ○

4.
○ ○ ○

5.
○ ○ ○

Name _____ Date _____ Score _____

Selection Vocabulary

1.    ◯   ◯   ◯

2.    ◯      ◯

3.    ◯      ◯

4.    ◯      ◯

5.    ◯         ◯

Name _____ **Date** _____ **Score** _____

Writing Assessment

_____

_____

_____

_____

_____

_____

_____

_____

_____

_____

_____

_____

_____

_____

_____

_____

_____

Name _____ **Date** _____ **Score** _____

Letters and Sounds

1. heut   heat   hoat
   ○   ○   ○

2. dule   dale   deal
   ○   ○   ○

3. hure   here   har
   ○   ○   ○

4. feet   fite   faet
   ○   ○   ○

5. east   iste   aste
   ○   ○   ○

Name _____ Date _____ Score _____

High-Frequency Words

1.   or   ur   er
       ○   ○   ○

2.   twi   tou   two
       ○   ○   ○

3.   bi   be   ba
       ○   ○   ○

4.   green   grien   geren
       ○   ○   ○

5.   tike   tayk   take
       ○   ○   ○

Name _____ **Date** _____ **Score** _____

Main Idea and Details

1.   farms   cows   trees
          ○   ○   ○

2.   river   ocean   lake
          ○   ○   ○

3.   stars   clouds   birds
          ○   ○   ○

4.   table   floor   chair
          ○   ○   ○

5.   cold   rainy   snowy
          ○   ○   ○

Name _____ **Date** _____ **Score** _____

Special Text

1. July 4   Karen   Dallas
        ○   ○   ○

2.   j   B   q
        ○   ○   ○

3.   100   3:30   big
        ○   ○   ○

4.   five   pick   moon
        ○   ○   ○

5. Betty's room   he isn't   one o'clock
        ○   ○   ○

Name _____ Date _____ Score _____

Letters and Sounds

1. hard   luck   sing
    ○   ○   ○

2. fish   five   fit
    ○   ○   ○

3. bank   list   math
    ○   ○   ○

4. party   ride   made
    ○   ○   ○

5. stamp   third   ledge
    ○   ○   ○

Name _____ **Date** _____ **Score** _____

High-Frequency Words

1.   evere   everi   every
         ○   ○   ○

2.   culde   could   couwd
         ○   ○   ○

3.   boy   boye   boi
         ○   ○   ○

4.   sume   some   somm
         ○   ○   ○

5.   goind   goeng   going
         ○   ○   ○

Name _____ **Date** _____ **Score** _____

Cause and Effect

1. backpack   late   lunch
         ○   ○   ○

2. sit   eat   run
         ○   ○   ○

3. cat   dog   Ben
         ○   ○   ○

4. leaves   rain   rugs
         ○   ○   ○

5. slipping   shoveling   walking
         ○   ○   ○

Name _____ **Date** _____ **Score** _____

Grammar, Usage, and Mechanics

1.   big   run   hat
       ○   ○   ○

2.   red   sit   taller
       ○   ○   ○

3.   hat   pens   lamp
       ○   ○   ○

4.   babies   sister   friend
       ○   ○   ○

5.   Me   Us   I
       ○   ○   ○

Name _____ Date _____ Score _____

Letters and Sounds

1.   fly   fla   flo
       ○   ○   ○

2.   sha   she   shu
       ○   ○   ○

3.   poni   pona   pony
       ○   ○   ○

4.   clay   clee   claj
       ○   ○   ○

5.   lute   leet   light
       ○   ○   ○

Name _____ **Date** _____ **Score** _____

High-Frequency Words

1. dey day dai
   ○   ○   ○

2. way wey wah
   ○   ○   ○

3. slepe sleap sleep
   ○   ○   ○

4. dun't don't dor't
   ○   ○   ○

5. my mi mu
   ○   ○   ○

Name _____ **Date** _____ **Score** _____

Sequence

1.

○   ○   ○

2.

○   ○   ○

3.

○   ○   ○

4.

○   ○   ○

5.

○   ○   ○

Name _____ Date _____ Score _____

Selection Vocabulary

1.

   ◯      ◯   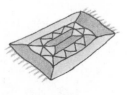   ◯

2.

   ◯      ◯      ◯

3.

   ◯      ◯      ◯

4.

   ◯      ◯

5.

◯   ◯   ◯

Name _____ **Date** _____ **Score** _____

Writing Assessment

_____

_____

_____

_____

_____

_____

_____

_____

Name _____ Date _____ Score _____

Letters and Sounds

1. race   ○   kind   ○   fire   ○

2. free   ○   chew   ○   pie   ○

3. tin   ○   tow   ○   ten   ○

4. few   ○   night   ○   walk   ○

5. mule   ○   steep   ○   oak   ○

Name _____ **Date** _____ **Score** _____

High-Frequency Words

1. on ○ ni ○ no ○

2. their ○ thire ○ theer ○

3. eway ○ away ○ awiy ○

4. tou ○ too ○ tew ○

5. came ○ caim ○ kame ○

Name _____ **Date** _____ **Score** _____

Compare and Contrast

1. 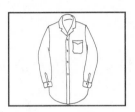  ◯  ◯

2. 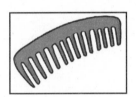  ◯  ◯

3.   ◯  ◯

4.   ◯  ◯

5. 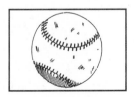  ◯ 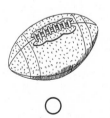 ◯

Name _____ Date _____ Score _____

Text Recognition

1. Joan saw Tim. She said hello. They went for a walk.

3	4	5
○	○	○

2.

Waldo	Bambi	"Heidi"
○	○	○

3.

Jamie	José	Judy
○	○	○

4.

on the beach	then . . . it rained	if we wanted
○	○	○

5. Some ducks landed on the pond.

pond	landed	Some
○	○	○

Name _____ **Date** _____ **Score** _____

Letters and Sounds

1.　few　　　　　tool　　　　　rot
　　　　○　　　　　　○　　　　　　○

2.　might　　　　gate　　　　　lap
　　　　○　　　　　　○　　　　　　○

3.　jet　　　　　not　　　　　　yes
　　　　○　　　　　　○　　　　　　○

4.　read　　　　pain　　　　　cool
　　　　○　　　　　　○　　　　　　○

5.　goat　　　　blue　　　　　won
　　　　○　　　　　　○　　　　　　○

Name _____ **Date** _____ **Score** _____

High-Frequency Words

1.   swa   saw   siw
         ○   ○   ○

2.   blue   belu   blwe
         ○   ○   ○

3.   onn   ine   one
         ○   ○   ○

4.   mi   me   mu
         ○   ○   ○

5.   right   ritte   righb
         ○   ○   ○

Name _____ Date _____ Score _____

Classify and Categorize

1.   cow   red   cold
○   ○   ○

2.   mouse   cat   dog
○   ○   ○

3.   car   book   skunk
○   ○   ○

4.   grass   boat   blue
○   ○   ○

5.   sun   breakfast   moon
○   ○   ○

Name _____ Date _____ Score _____

Grammar, Usage, and Mechanics

1.   Must   June   Them

○   ○   ○

2.   .   ?   !

○   ○   ○

3. Ben travels by train. Ben travels by bus.

Ben travels by   Ben travels   Ben likes

train and bus.   to travel.

○   ○   ○

4. A big storm hit <u>ames iowa</u>.

Ames Iowa   ames, iowa   Ames, Iowa

○   ○   ○

5. My sister was born on <u>april 10 2003</u>.

april 10, 2003   April, 10 2003   April 10, 2003

○   ○   ○

Name _____ **Date** _____ **Score** _____

Letters and Sounds

1. mowd   moad   mood
    ○   ○   ○

2. role   rowl   rule
    ○   ○   ○

3. crow   crou   croo
    ○   ○   ○

4. chew   chei   chou
    ○   ○   ○

5. bouk   book   bowk
    ○   ○   ○

Name _____ Date _____ Score _____

High-Frequency Words

1.   vere   viry   very

    ○   ○   ○

2.   guod   good   goot

    ○   ○   ○

3.   now   niw   nwo

    ○   ○   ○

4.   here   heer   hier

    ○   ○   ○

5.   jo   gi   go

    ○   ○   ○

Name _____ **Date** _____ **Score** _____

Making Inferences

1. gardening   painting   moving
    ○   ○   ○

2. walk   swim   eat
    ○   ○   ○

3. hammer   broom   pliers
    ○   ○   ○

4. beach   movie   mall
    ○   ○   ○

5. morning   noon   afternoon
    ○   ○   ○

Name _____ **Date** _____ **Score** _____

Selection Vocabulary

1.  ◯   ◯   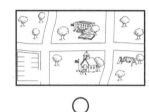 ◯

2.  ◯    ◯   ◯

3. ◯    ◯    ◯

4.  ◯   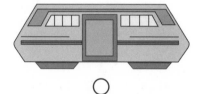 ◯    ◯

5.  ◯   ◯    ◯

Name _____ **Date** _____ **Score** _____

Writing Assessment

_____

_____

_____

_____

_____

_____

_____

_____

_____

_____

_____

_____

_____

_____

_____

_____